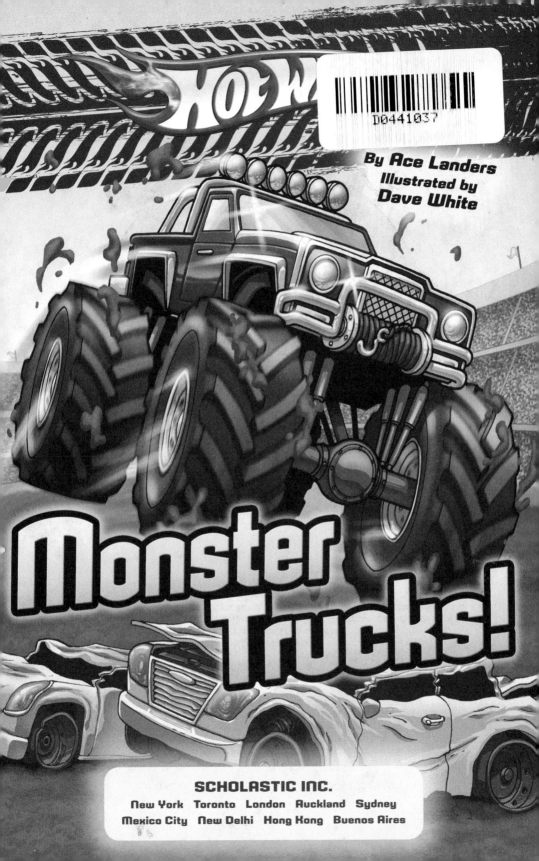

By Ace Landers
Illustrated by
Dave White

D0441037

Monster Trucks!

SCHOLASTIC INC.
New York Toronto London Auckland Sydney
Mexico City New Delhi Hong Kong Buenos Aires

ISBN-10: 0-545-11040-8
ISBN-13: 978-0-545-11040-2

Published by Scholastic Inc. SCHOLASTIC and associated logos
are trademarks and/or registered trademarks of Scholastic Inc.

12 11 10 9 8 7 6 5   9 10 11 12 13 14/0

Printed in the U.S.A.
First printing, January 2009

Welcome to the monster truck show!

The monster trucks are huge!

They are ready to drive over anything.

Monster truck tires
are as big as a car.

The tires help monster trucks drive over big hills.

Here is a row of old cars.

The yellow monster truck takes the lead.

It speeds up the ramp.

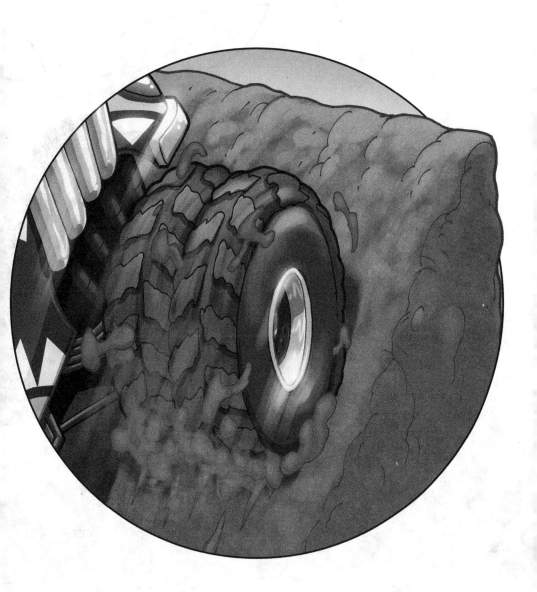

The truck flies over the cars!

The red monster truck drives
on top of the old cars!

A green truck is racing
around the track.

The green truck and the red truck almost crash!

Both trucks spin out.

The green truck rises on
two wheels.

The monster trucks land safely.

There is no time to stop!

The orange truck gets ready.

Another monster truck revs its engine.

The orange truck sails over the cars and the blue truck!

The blue truck rolls and
bounces on the old cars.

The orange truck lands perfectly.

The blue truck has a problem!

Will the blue truck land safely?

It lands safely!
The driver is in control!

Every truck is on the track.

The crowd goes wild!

Monster trucks rule!